Race Day Blues

Mandie Schrader

illustrated by Kabita Studios

Race Day Blues
A Hawaiian Heritage Critter Collection Book
Written by Mandie Schrader
Illustrated by Kabita Studios

Copyright © 2018, Mandie Schrader
First Edition, September 2018

Published By
   White Parrot Press,
   an imprint of First Steps Publishing
   PO Box 571
   Gleneden Beach, OR 97388-0571
   FirstStepsPublishing.com

Library of Congress Control Number: 2018947910

Schrader, Mandie

Race Day Blues
A Hawaiian Heritage Critter Collection Book

Gleneden Beach, OR., First Steps Publishing., © 2018.

ISBN: 978-1-937333-63-8 (pbk); 978-1-937333-76-8 (hbk)

Summary: Steve is a centipede who loves to run in races, but his feet always blister and are sore after each event. His sister, Sarah, whose passion is designing shoes, makes him shoes for his next race. When his laces come untied during the event, Steve falls and loses. Steve is still happy and considers the race a win because his feet do not hurt! Steve's story ends with him asking his sister to make another pair of shoes for him, but this time without laces.

1. Siblings--Juvenile fiction / Family / Siblings.
2. Humor--Juvenile fiction / Humorous Stories.
3. Insects, Spiders, etc.--Juvenile fiction / Animals.
4. Competition--Juvenile fiction / Sports & Recreation / General.
5. Beginning Reader -- Juvenile Fiction
I. Title.

an imprint of
First Steps Publishing

Printed in the U.S.A.

To Riley Bug –
Here's your bug book.

And to my mom –
We did it!

There are bugs that cling
And bugs that sing
And bugs with lots of eyes

There are bugs that dig
That look like twigs
And even bugs that fly

Among all of these
Who do things with ease
Steve's not your average guy

Though he's stuck on the ground
And his body's quite round
Our Steve is incredibly spry

In all the bug races
He always outpaces
He's known for his
outrageous speed

Legs he has plenty
Way more than twenty
For Steve is a centipede

Now all of those feet
You may think are neat
In races you always would score

But Steve had the thought
Winning isn't so hot
If your feet are always sore

His sister once said
"Steve get out of bed
This race is one of a kind"

But Steve, he refused
His feet were so bruised
He knew they would leave
him behind

Now Sarah was smart
And had a big heart
She wouldn't let her
brother lose

She had a passion
For one kind of fashion
Her love was designing shoes

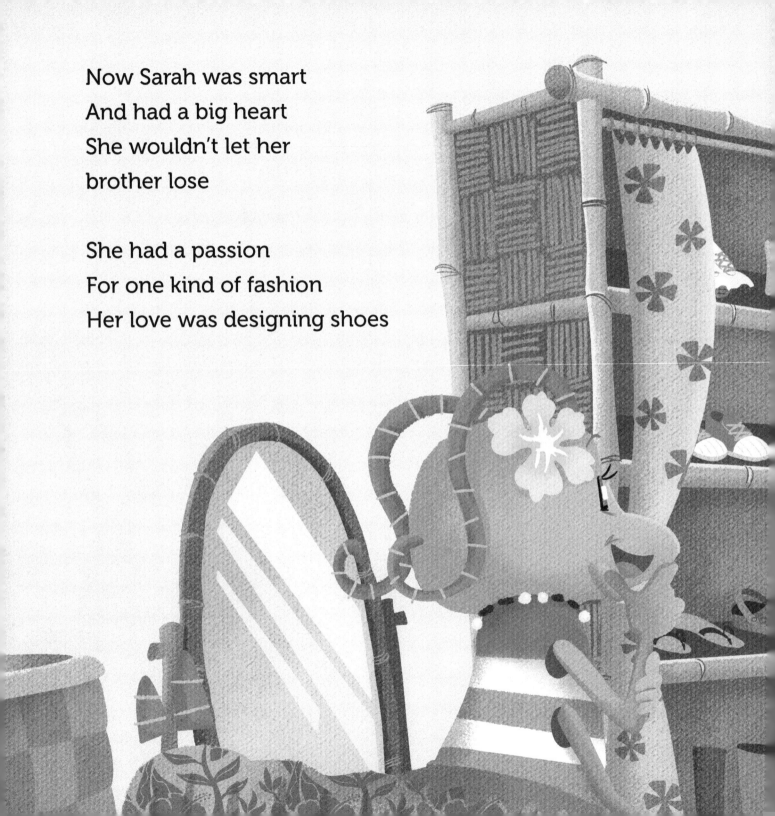

For days she drew
Shoe after shoe
No rest until it was right

A sole that was springy
With sides that weren't clingy
And laces that weren't too tight

On the day of the race
In Sarah's embrace
She told Steve
she had a surprise

She showed him the shoes,
Said "I know you can't lose"
Her faith brought tears
to his eyes.

APRIL
15
Race Day!

At the start of the race
Steve watched his pace
Breathlessly awaiting the ache

As he continued to run
In the hot island sun
The competition was left
in his wake

Around the first curve
He didn't swerve
His feet ran straight and true

He let out a yell
"Gee this is swell!"
Through the rest of the race
he just flew

In the final lap
There was a huge gap
Between him and the
closest contender

But he tripped on a lace
Fell flat on his face
The lead he may have
to surrender

At the finish line
He was slightly outshined
By a bug whose shoes didn't tie

Steve only shrugged
His sister he hugged
And let out a happy sigh

To Sarah he said
"I used to dread
Walking home after the races

Today there's no pain
Not even a strain
But next time let's go
with no laces"

Did You Know...?

The word **Centipede** comes from Latin: **centi-** meaning <u>hundred</u> and **pedis** – meaning <u>foot</u>.

Centipedes are arthropods. This means they are invertebrates (have no spine), have an exoskeleton (a hard, outer shell), have segmented bodies, and jointed legs.

Centipedes have one pair of legs per body segment. They can have fewer than 20 legs or more then 300!

Centipedes always have an odd number pair of legs. They can have 19 pairs or 21 pairs, but never 20 pairs.

Centipedes can get up to 12 inches in length!

Centipedes are mostly nocturnal, meaning they're awake all night and sleep during the day.

Centipedes are usually red and/or brown in color, but are also known to be yellow, green, or even blue.

Centipedes generally eat earthworms, insects, and spiders. Some of the bigger species are known to eat reptiles, amphibians, small mammals such as bats, and even birds.

Centipedes inject their prey with venom. Their bite causes pain, swelling, and sometimes chills and fever in humans, but it is rarely fatal.

Centipedes are food for mongooses, mice, salamanders, snakes, beetles, and birds.

An avid reader with an overactive imagination, Mandie Schrader has been creating worlds and telling stories since childhood. She is a YA Librarian in Hawaii where she enjoys the beach, hiking in the wilderness, and crafting works of fiction about bugs, fairies, and the complexities of love and life in general.

Learn more about Mandie Schrader and check out all the great "Team Steve" merchandise at AmandaSchrader.com

9 781937 333638